H.P. LOVECRAFT'S
The CALL of CTHULHU

for beginning readers

By R.J. Ivankovic

H.P. LOVECRAFT'S THE CALL OF CTHULHU
FOR BEGINNING READERS
© 2017 Richard John Ivankovic. All rights reserved.
This edition © 2017 Chaosium, Inc. All rights reserved.

Call of Cthulhu is a registered trademark of Chaosium, Inc.

chaosium.com

978-1-56882-112-2

Third printing, July 2020
9 8 7 6 5 4 3

For

Howard, Theodor,

Allison, and Maximilian.

I

The Horror in Clay

The most merciful thing

in the world, I believe,

is humanity's failure

to fully conceive

of the cosmical horrors

we've yet to reveal,

and which up until now

I have tried to conceal.

Back in late '26,
when my great-uncle died,
I discovered the research
he wanted to hide.

Over time he'd uncovered
much more than he should.
He'd have kept it all secret
if only he could.

But Professor George Angell
has met with his fate,
and exactly what killed him
has caused some debate.

The physicians have claimed
there's no reason to doubt
that his lengthy walk home
caused his heart to give out.

The more sinister truth,

I have heard people say:

He was shoved by a sailor

who stood in his way.

And my poor uncle, George,

he was really too old

to survive such a bump

on a hill in the cold.

Shortly after his death
on that hill by the sea,
the professor's belongings
were given to me.

I was sorting through all
of his research one day,
when I found a monstrosity
made out of clay.

It was carved by a sculptor
named Wilcox one night,
when more sensitive folk
endured horrible sights.

The young sculptor was puzzled
by what he had made,
by the script and the creature
his carving displayed.

So he sought out an expert
who'd know what they meant,
who'd explain his mad visions
and where his mind went.

It was fortune that brought him
to Angell's front door.

You see, Angell had seen
such a creature before.

The professor urged Wilcox

to try and recall

all the things he had dreamed of,

no matter how small.

When the sculptor then coughed up

the sounds that he'd heard,

it confirmed something quite

supernatural occurred.

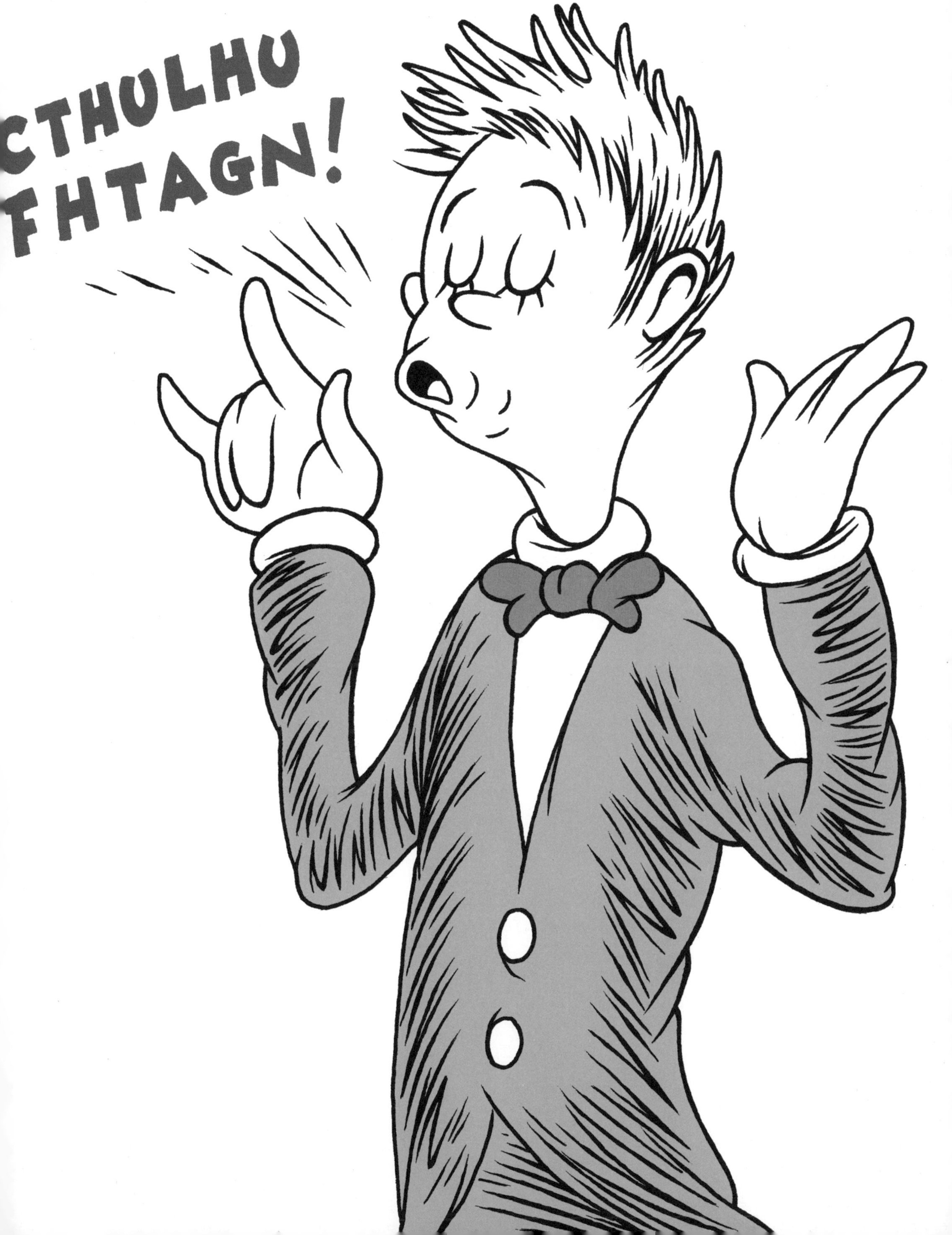
CTHULHU
FHTAGN!

The professor requested

a journal be kept,

that the sculptor could update

each night that he slept.

And the dreamer recorded

the things he had seen

for the whole month of March

with this nightly routine.

But on April the 2nd

his diary stopped,

when into unconsciousness

Wilcox had dropped.

I believed it was probably
some kind of hoax —
that my uncle fell victim
to Wilcox's jokes.

For a time I was willing
to let it all pass,
until later I read of
Inspector Legrasse.

II

The Tale of Inspector Legrasse

When Legrasse met with
experts who liked to explore,
he presented a thing
they had not seen before.

He was looking for answers,
but got none at all,
until Webb raised his hand
at the back of the hall.

He had seen

something like it

a long time ago.

It was worshipped
in Greenland by
strange Esquimaux.

PH'NGLUI MGLW'NAFH CTHULHU

He described how they danced

and repeated their cries,

which Legrasse recognized

to the experts' surprise.

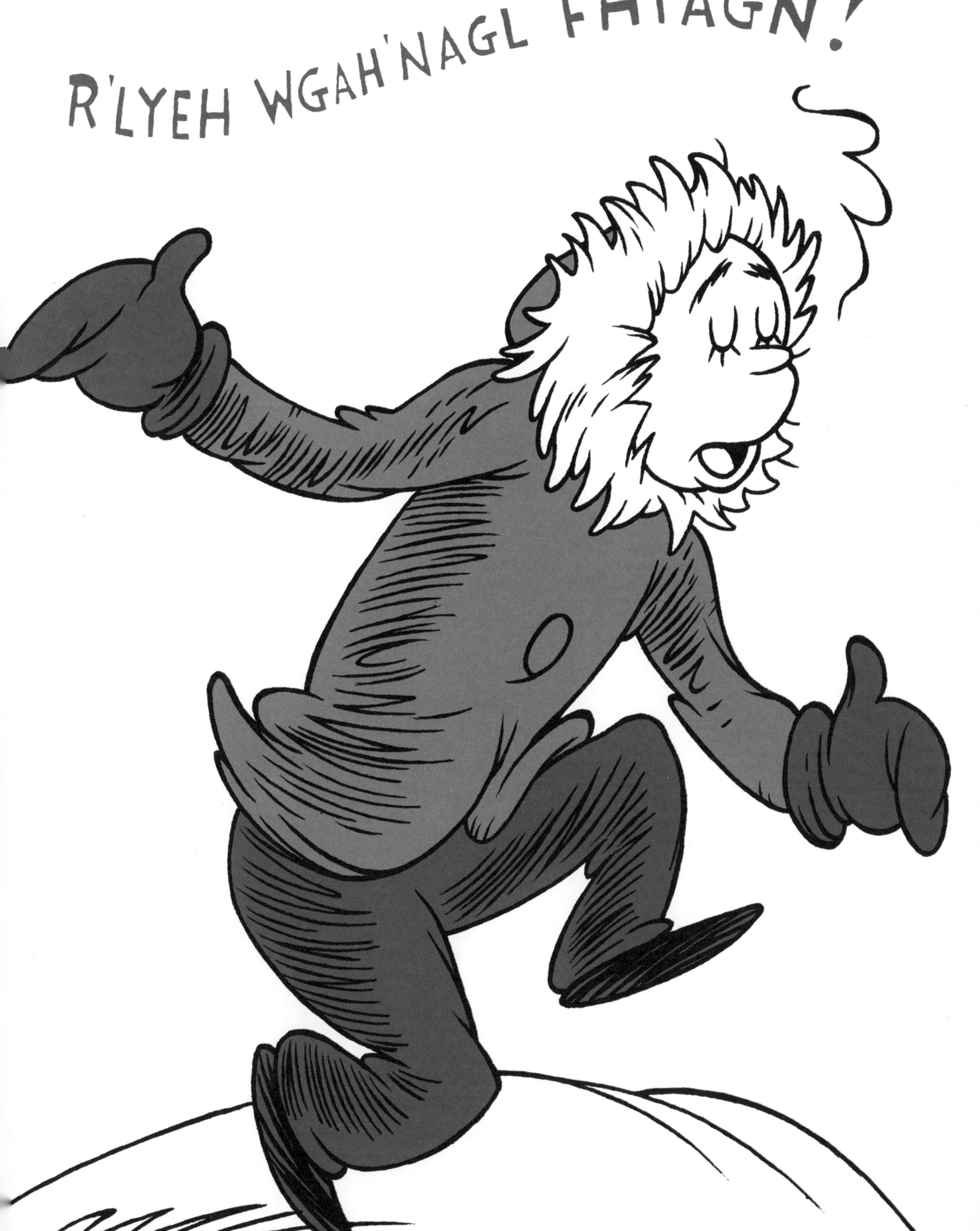
R'LYEH WGAH'NAGL FHTAGN!

He went on to reveal
where his knowledge
was gained:
he'd encountered a cult,
the inspector explained.

They had told him the meaning
of the words they'd been screaming:
"In his house at R'lyeh,
dead Cthulhu waits dreaming."

In a New Orleans swamp,
less than one year before,
he had broken that cult
in the name of the law.

When some people who lived
near that swamp disappeared,
the police had been called,
and the worst had been feared.

There were rumours of crimes

being kept out of sight

in the heart of the swamp,

in the midst of the night.

So Legrasse had arranged

for a squad of brave men

to accompany him

to the maniacs' den.

The policemen took care
to avoid certain trails,
as the locals had told them
some terrible tales.

They were warned of a lake
and its polypous thing,
to which cultists at midnight
would crazily sing.

When Legrasse and his men
had uncovered the place,
they discovered the worst
of the whole human race.

The policemen had paused
to recover their breath.

All the kidnapping victims
had been put to death.

With the cultists locked up

by the end of the day,

the police had to know

why they'd acted that way.

Then a cultist named Castro

had spoken with glee,

when describing a city

lost under the sea.

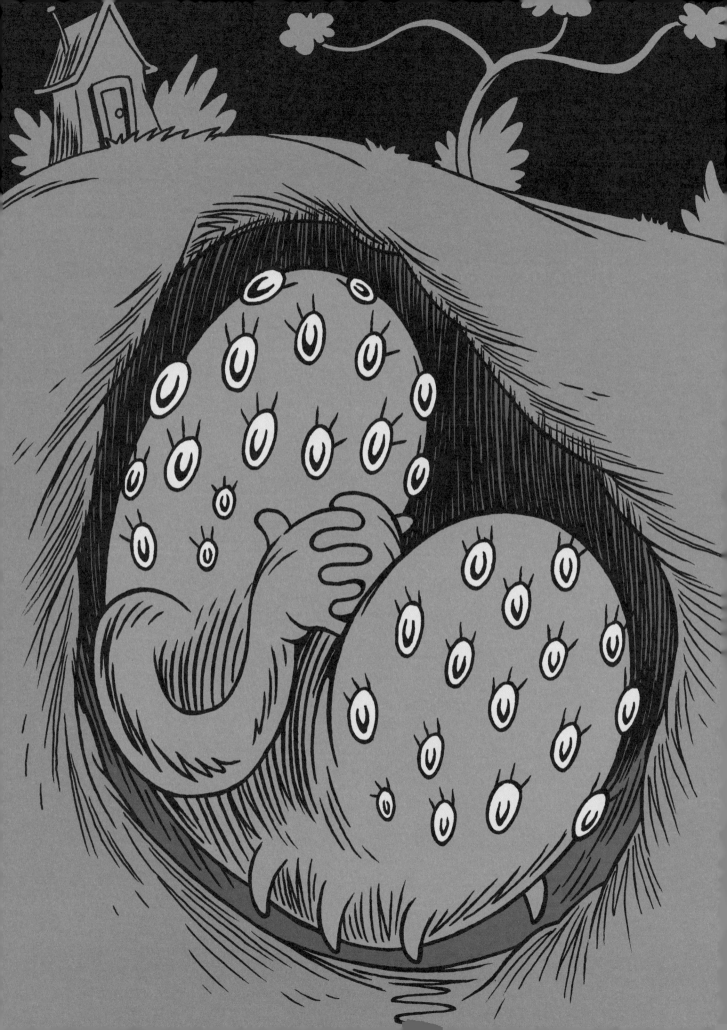

He believed that
Great Old Ones,
who lie underground,
will remain there until
that lost city is found.

Great Cthulhu once led them
across outer space,
when they flew here to Earth
from some faraway place.

They have slept for millennia,
Castro had said,
but their dreaming confirms
that they're really not dead.

When that city, named R'lyeh,
comes up from the deep,
then Cthulhu will stir
and give up his great sleep.

You'll find mention of this,
if you dare take a look,
inside Abdul Alhazred's
mysterious book.

I will quote here verbatim,
for those who don't know,
what that mad Arab wrote
such a long time ago:

There is nothing that's dead
which can eternal lie,
because give it strange aeons
and death may yet die.

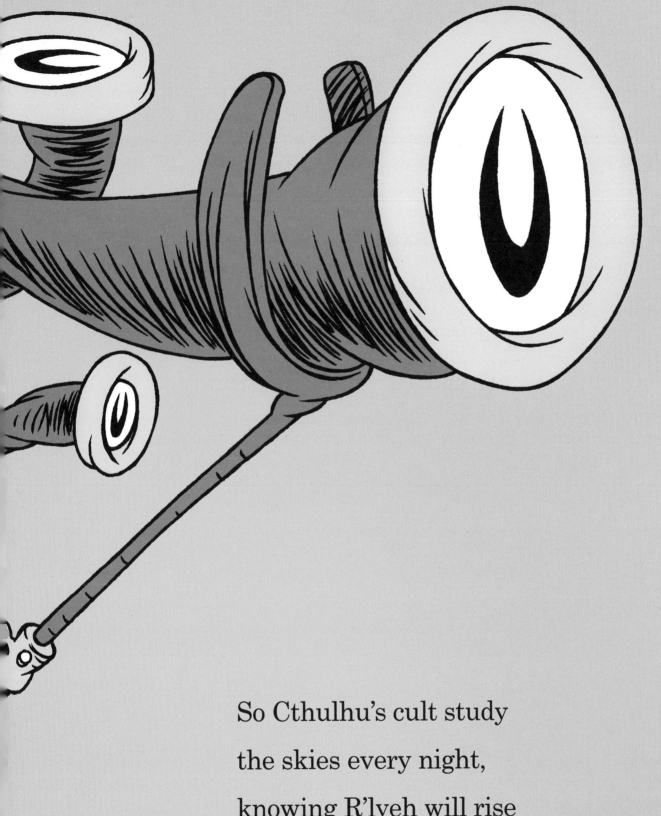

So Cthulhu's cult study
the skies every night,
knowing R'lyeh will rise
when the stars are just right.

All the experts, and Angell,

had taken an oath

not to speak of that cult,

nor encourage its growth.

With the mad implications

of what they had heard,

they would research in secret

and not say a word.

It was hard to believe
all the things that I'd read.
I still doubted a lot
of what Wilcox had said.

I had thought that perhaps
the young sculptor had heard
of that dark Southern swamp
and the crime that occurred.

For my own peace of mind
I just had to be sure
that it wasn't a prank,
that it was something more.

When I'd spoken to Wilcox
he'd made it quite clear
that the call of Cthulhu
was something to fear.

Then I went to see Castro,

but Castro was dead,

so I stopped in to see

the inspector instead.

When I spoke to Legrasse

I was lucky to find

that he still had the cult

in the back of his mind.

I had started to think

it would make my career

if I published this stuff

for the whole world to hear.

I believed I could research
and then write a book,
but with no further leads
there was nowhere to look.

So I packed up my notes
and I put them aside.

It was only much later
a clue was supplied.

III

The Madness from the Sea

I was studying rocks

from all over the world,

when a sheet of old newsprint

from Sydney unfurled.

On that faded old page

a forgotten report

told the tale of a schooner

whose trip was cut short.

Of eleven crew members,

ten failed to return,

and the loss of the *Emma*

had caused some concern.

After meeting a yacht,
which had ordered them back,
it appears that the *Emma*
fell under attack.

When the *Emma* was sunk
there was nothing to do
but to seize the *Alert*
and abandon her crew.

Two weeks later, in Sydney,
a sailor arrived,
but no other crewmen
from the *Emma* survived.

The report said Johansen
returned from the sea
with an idol in hand,
quite mysteriously.

On the fate of his crew
he'd refused to say more
than they'd died on an island
they'd stopped to explore.

The events had occurred
in the very same week
that young Wilcox's nightmares
had been at their peak.

So I tracked down Johansen
to hear what he'd say
through New Zealand, and Sydney,
and lastly Norway.

When Mrs. Johansen
had come to his door
she explained that he'd died
just a few months before.

He had never revealed
what had happened at sea,
so she took out his logbook
and gave it to me.

He had written in English
to help spare his wife
from the terrible knowledge
that ruined his life.

In that book he described
the strange place he had seen,
and I knew that to R'lyeh
the sailor had been.

When the crew went ashore
they discovered a stair,
so they climbed to the top
just to see what was there.

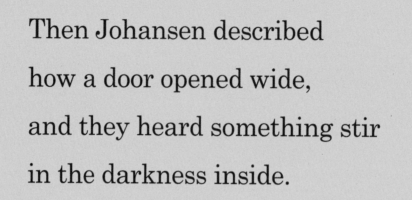

Then Johansen described
how a door opened wide,
and they heard something stir
in the darkness inside.

He recalled that they froze,
and that nobody spoke,
so intense was their fear
when...

Cthulhu

awoke.

When Johansen and Briden
returned to the sea,
they had jumped in their boat
in an effort to flee.

As Johansen prepared
to escape in the yacht,
he discovered the boiler
was not very hot.

When the sailors then learned
that Cthulhu could swim,
poor old Briden went mad
and the future looked grim.

The *Alert* started moving,
but not very fast,
and the creature drew closer
each moment that passed.

There was nothing to do
but to steer with the wheel
till Cthulhu's huge head
was lined up with the keel.

When the yacht pierced Cthulhu
between his great eyes,
the *Alert* had survived,
to Johansen's surprise.

At the end of the logbook
I fearfully read
that the monster was sighted
repairing his head.

By the time they were rescued
poor Briden had died,
and Johansen was sitting
with eyes open wide.

Then the rescue ship, *Vigilant*,
sailed past the spot
where the city once was,
but by then it was not.

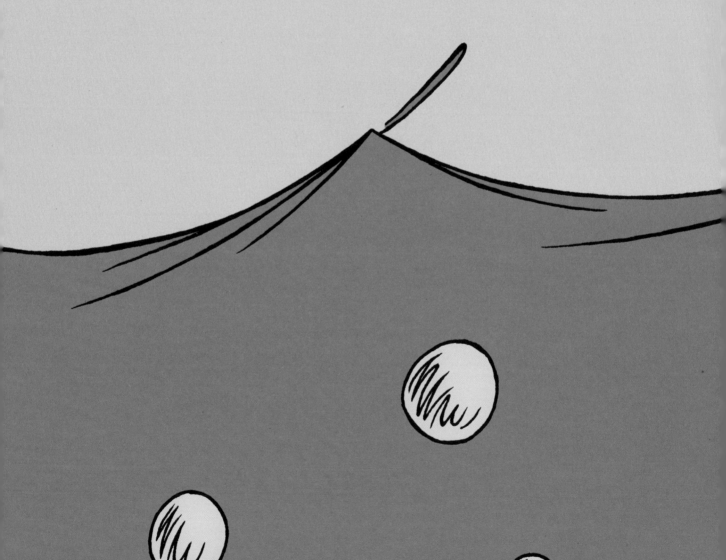

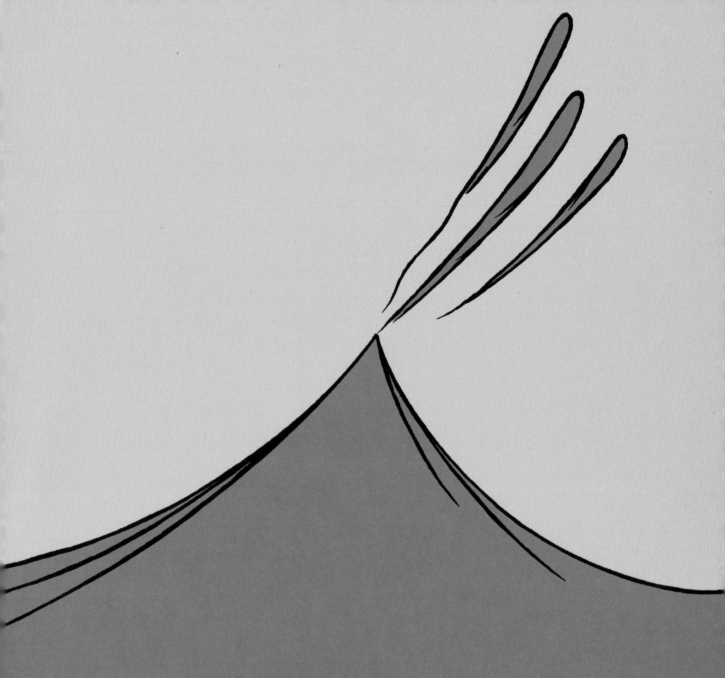

I assume that Cthulhu
resumed his great sleep
at the heart of his city
way down in the deep.

I discovered the sender
of Wilcox's dreams,
and I'm certain there's more
to the cult than it seems.

But the knowledge is more
than just one man can take,
and, in knowing, I fear
that my mind will soon break.

Now I've told you these things
so that you'll understand
why I'm sealing them up,
just as Angell had planned.

Just remember the cultists are out there somewhere, keeping track of the secrets they don't want to share.

*Found Among the Papers
of the Late
Francis Wayland Thurston,
of Boston.*